W9-DJI-920

MENTAL HEALTH
RECOVERY BOOSTERS

How to Sustain Your Mental Wellness

Carol A. Kivler, MS, CSP

Recovery is the goal —

Carol Kivler

2013

Mental Health Recovery Boosters
How to Sustain Your Mental Wellness

Carol A. Kivler, MS, CSP

Published by:
Three Gem Publishing/Kivler Communications

(609) 882-8988

Cover and Inside Layout: Singles Design
Courageous Recovery Logo: Jack Out of the Box

Printed in the United States of America

IBSN: 978-0-9844799-2-4

Dedication

To my six beautiful grandchildren -
J.R., Peyton, Carter, Austen, Hunter, and Grant.
You are my true "joy boosters" in life, and Grammy
loves each of you.

Acknowledgements

I would like to acknowledge Karen Meltzer, my marketing and right hand assistant. Karen came to Courageous Recovery three years ago and has been a driving force in getting our message out. No job big or small is an effort for Karen. Her astute researching skills, her ability to uncover who she needs to speak to in an association or organization, her enthusiasm and personal belief that it's time to combat stigma surrounding mental health disorders fuels the energy needed for us to keep moving forward. Karen took the lead as project manager on this book and kept everyone on deadline. With Karen's help this book project not only stayed on track, it remained a pleasant experience.

My next acknowledgement goes out to our social media team, Susan Critelli and Terry Andrews. This dynamic duo is responsible for creating and maintaining our digital footprint. We depend heavily on their expertise and business sense of where and what we should be doing in the social media arena. Their keen and up-to-date entries on my blog site, Facebook, Twitter and Pinterest bring the latest on mental health topics to our followers.

Finally, a big thank you to all the consumers and family members who continue to reach out to me for answers and inspiration. Their "reach outs" have provided an avenue for me to live my life purpose – to help change the face of mental illness to a face of mental wellness.

Essays

Introduction

For more years than I can remember, I've started each day reading two devotional books. These readings jumpstart my day with inspiration and reflection. But more importantly, I find taking time to invest in my mental wellness for the day provides the positive energy I need to embark on a better day.

What I've learned over the years is the power of one's beliefs. We have all heard of the self-fulfilling prophecy – if you think you can or you think you can't, you prove yourself right on either side. Why? You build your reality upon thoughts you agree are true. Also, you have it within your power to tap into two universal laws: The Laws of Intention and Attraction. Once you set your intention to mental wellness, providence takes over and you attract experiences and opportunities to live the life you created with your intentions.

My intention for this book is to share the greatest lessons life has offered me through a variety of short essays. Twelve years ago, I embarked on moving from mental illness into the realm of mental wellness. It was though a light switch had been turned on in my life. I was entrenched in the medical model of mental illness, and it was not sustaining my recovery for longer than four years at a time. What I found I needed was an attitude shift – a shift from illness to wellness. Your attention to wellness makes the biggest difference in dealing with any illness.

This book is different in that you do not need to read it from cover to cover. Instead I encourage you to sit down once a day or once a week in silence and ask God to provide the guidance you need at that given moment. Thumb through the pages until you feel an urge to stop and read. Each essay sits by itself with a message of inspiration and reflection. If you are like me, you might want to read the message a second time so it has time to sink into your conscious mind before moving onto answering the reflection question. Answering the question helps you transfer the commitment of wellness to your own life.

Finally, my hope for you is that you will be inspired enough to hold yourself personally accountable for your own mental wellness. When you take the time to answer the reflection questions, you will be setting your wellness intentions out into the universe to manifest the life you were meant to live.

Thank you for allowing me to be part of your wellness journey!

*Time to embark on moving from
mental illness into the realm
of mental wellness*

Recovery Takes Personal Responsibility

"Recovery is a process of change through which individuals improve their health and wellness, live a self-directed life, and strive to reach their full potential."

-Substance Abuse and Mental Health Services Administration (SAMHSA)

Many health professionals are still tied to the old model of treating people with mental health disorders. However, I am beginning to see movement towards a new model – a model of recovery. Fortunately, SAMHSA, a national organization working to reduce the impact mental illness has in our communities, has a director who is extremely familiar with recovery – he has recovered from his own mental health disorders and knows firsthand how recovery occurs.

The new model focuses on recovery not as a fixed destination but as an on-going process you work on every day. Symptom remission, while important, is just one step in the process of personal growth and recovery. By mapping out a richer, more satisfying existence, SAMHSA has identified a four-part harmony that contributes to successful recovery.

Health – managing or overcoming your disorder and living in a physically and emotionally healthy way.

Home – maintaining a stable and safe place to live.

Purpose – pursuing meaningful activities, such as, working at a job, volunteering, going to school.

Community – having relationships and networks that provide support, comfort, encouragement, and hope.

The recovery model is both self-directed and person-centered, placing as much of the responsibility and accountability on the consumer as it does on other facets. I believe that, for most people, once you internalize this new model, and do what's in your own power to embrace these concepts, recovery is within reach. And I will continue, with every ounce of my being, to remain in recovery because the alternative is too heavy a personal price to pay.

Reflection Question: *In which area of this four-part harmony do you need to ask for help?*

Take the First Step

*"Never bend your head. Always hold it high.
Look the world straight in the face."*

– Helen Keller

Depression and anxiety have a way of isolating us from the world and robbing us of self-confidence. When I read this quote, it was a wake-up call for me to recognize the power in facing the symptoms of an illness that haunts way too many of our lives.

These simple reminders could be the first stepping-stones to help us re-enter life. Just the thought of going out into the world when we feel like everyone else's life is running smoothly and ours is a disaster can be a frightening thought. But one thing I've come to realize is that no one – except me – can take that first step.

So today, I've decided to face the world in spite of the symptoms of an illness that has stolen way too many days from my life. Today I will regain some of my personal power to live the life God promised me.

I encourage each of you to take a deep breath, hold your head high, and walk out the door knowing that you, too, can take that first step towards regaining your place in the world!

Reflection Question: *What will it take for you to open that door and take the first step outside?*

Pay Attention

"I think the one lesson I have learned is that there is no substitute for paying attention."

– Diane Sawyer

Starting any new year, you have control over many things – but not everything. As the quote states, paying attention is the key.

For those of us with an ailment that shows up when it's not invited, it's critical to regularly – if not daily – monitor where you are mentally and physically. You've got to pay attention!

I've learned that my body gives me signals, if I would only stop long enough to notice them. For instance, when I experience sleep disruption and racing thoughts or an increasingly dreadful feeling, I know I must pay attention before I can barely function. I've learned that ignoring these changes, doesn't mean they will disappear on their own.

When you pay attention and then start getting those signals, what do you do? First, recognize that you need help. These aren't disorders you should try to fix on your own. Reach out to your healthcare professional – an adjustment to your treatment plan and medications might lessen the length of a relapse. And there are many other things you can control that will help: your schedule, exercise, choice of friends, what you read, watch, and listen to, how you speak to yourself, where you spend your time, and finally what you do to help others. But the real key is to first pay attention.

This coming year, pay attention to how you feel mentally and physically and to all the little things that fill your life with a spirit of happiness. It's worth your effort!

Reflection Question: *What do you need to pay attention to?*

_____

_____

_____

_____

Focus on Recovery

*"When we have diluted focus,
we get diluted results."*

– Rory Vaden

This quote is a reminder that we each need to heed when it comes to staying in mental wellness. Since recovery is an on-going process, it takes focus and discipline to stay the course. Yet, the pace of life and the distractions that bombard often get in the way. So, what's a person to do to stay focused?

1. **Create a very vivid picture of your goal in your mind.**
   The picture of my recovery goal includes being able to enjoy life by participating in life – including remaining close to family and friends, sharing my abilities, staying out of the hospital, and fulfilling my dreams. How do you picture your goal?

2. **Pull together your support team.**
   Share your goal with others that you know and trust. Then seek their guidance and support as you work towards your goal. Life is too hard to go it alone. With

other people on your team, it's easier to stay focused on your recovery efforts.

3. **Hold yourself accountable for the essentials needed to reach recovery.**
   Over and over, we've heard what it takes to remain in recovery: acceptance of your disorder, treatment commitment, exercise, nutrition, sleep protection, and stress coping strategies. You know it, now you need to do it.

Are there days when I fall short? You bet. However, staying focused on recovery is a choice. Instead of beating myself up, I choose to refocus my energy and move on. You see, like many of you, I've come to recognize that life is just too short to try to be perfect.

Reflection Question: *What would it take for you to choose a focus of recovery?*

_____

_____

_____

_____

The Truth Will Set You Free

"Facts do not cease to exist because they are ignored."

– Aldous Huxley

I had an interesting conversation in Grand Rapids, Michigan with a woman, who for the first time revealed a secret that had haunted her for years. What was her secret? She said that when she struggled with depression and was consumed with suicidal ideation, she wanted to take her children with her in her plan to end it all. She had never told anyone about her plan, and the only reason she shared it with me was because I had talked about the same plan in my presentation she attended earlier in the day.

She had never heard another mother openly admit to wanting to take her children with her. I explained that my thoughts came from a loving concern, not selfishness. And at the time, I questioned, "who could possibility love my children as much as I do, and – who would take care of them if I were gone?" She said, "I asked myself those same questions." Finally, she sighed deeply with relief after revealing her haunting secret.

When we live in shame and guilt – like this mother had been doing for years – it's like living with a cancer that eats away at our self-worth and confidence. Living deep within this woman's subconscious was a secret she was too ashamed to admit to anyone. Finally, by telling her story, she released a burden she buried deep within her soul.

Little did I know that by sharing my own story – and my own truth – I would help set another person free.

Reflection Question: *What secret about your illness is haunting you?*

_____

_____

_____

_____

Look for the Meaning Behind All Experiences

"The need to find meaning...is as real as the need for trust and love, for relations with other human beings."

– Margaret Mead

I had the privilege of speaking at the Key Consumer Conference in Indianapolis. This organization serves 700 consumers challenged by mental health disorders in Indiana. One of the benefits of speaking at such conferences is that I learn as much from the attendees' mental health journeys as they learn from my own experiences.

Following my keynote, three consumers shared their stories during a breakout workshop. In the telling of their stories they brought meaning to their experiences. As we listened, we all recognized that through their sharing they were healing their broken spirits and lessening their painful memories.

Personally, I often questioned the reasoning behind my struggles with depression and anxiety. Meaning for me didn't appear until I, too, started telling my story. The more vulnerable I became with my story, the more I opened myself to healing the deep wounds in my spirit and my soul.

At the conference we witnessed people who were healing right before our eyes. One courageous man and two courageous women stood bravely in front of a roomful of eager listeners and revealed their darkest, most trying times without fear or shame. Based on the comments and questions the audience raised after they shared their stories, it was clear that the speakers *and* the audience members left the room with lighter burdens. The meaning of their journeys was revealed – it was to provide hope to those still fighting the good fight!

Reflection Question: *What stops you from sharing your own story?*

Treasures in Disguise

*"Our trials and difficulties are not here to break us. On the contrary, we seek them out to gain wisdom and to grow. They are **treasures in disguise**. We are not in tribulation but in transformation."*

– Hans Wilhelm

As I searched for this week's quote, I came across a book I first read in 2007 titled, *The Book of Courage.* This book directs us to look within ourselves and find courage at times when our entire world seems to be falling down around us. Courage is a sought after quality for anyone living with a life-long illness. As a matter of fact, the book reminds us that courage is something you need to survive life – period!

In the past you may have found yourself needing courage to face your fears, courage to take risks, courage to fight the good fight, even courage to just get through the day. Courage allows you to face your mental health disorder head on and move on in spite of past relapses or fear of future episodes.

16

Unfortunately though, some experiences in life are painful memories that if left alone continue to hamper your ability to engage in life to its fullest. Therefore, it is in your best interest to reframe those memories by asking yourself, "What did I learn?" and "How have I grown?" As Wilhelm's quote states, "*difficulties are treasures in disguise.*" If you dust off the cobwebs, and polish your difficult memories with a different perspective, your memories have an opportunity to become the true *treasures* they are meant to be.

Over the next week, take time to tap into the courage that lives within you. Then take a deep breath, and explore a past difficult time in your life. You will begin to recognize how the difficult time helped transform you into the person you are today.

Reflection Question: *Using your courage, what difficult time can you explore and turn into a treasure?*

Courage Is the Antidote to Hopelessness

"Grant me the courage not to give up even though I think it is hopeless."

– Chester W. Nimitz

Those of us dealing with a mental health disorder know all too well what it feels like to be hopeless – that dreaded feeling that we have nothing left to live for. Hopelessness is all-consuming *and* life threatening.

Because hopelessness is a symptom of all mental illnesses, it is essential that we recognize the antidote – ***courage***. With courage we can face the demons and darkness of an illness that robs us of our God-given right to share our talents with others.

So how do you embrace courage to break the cycle of hopelessness?

1. Remind yourself that "hopelessness" is a symptom of the illness, *not* a permanent condition.

2. Seek help and support the moment the "ugly head of hopelessness" appears.

3. Pray for courage and trust that you are not alone – God stands beside you.

4. Recall going through a past "hopeless episode" and remember how you recaptured your life.

When I think of the many people I know who have battled with mental illnesses for years, I define them as courageous survivors. They've fought the good fight with hopelessness, found the antidote in courage and won again and again. Let's learn to acknowledge each other's courage and appreciate the results – **a life that is to be lived and shared**!

Reflection Question: *Who do you know as a "courageous survivor" of mental illness?* ***Reach out to them today!***

It's Up to *You* to Seize the Moment

"You can wait forever for the right moment or you can make this moment the right one."

– C. Leslie Charles

Have you ever heard yourself say, *"I have to wait until I feel better or am fully recovered before I…?"* or *"I don't feel well enough to…"* There were many times in my mental health journey when I limited my involvement in the world and my life because I didn't push forward and seize the day before me. I bet you can say the same thing too.

Now I recognize that I can make *any* day into the day I want it to be. If I wake up tired because I didn't sleep well, I can still get to the gym. Then something almost magical happens. As I exercise and push through my fatigue, I begin to feel energized. Maybe it's the endorphins flowing through my body or the conversation I have with the woman next to me on the treadmill. **All I know is that my attitude toward the day ahead does an "about face."**

So what about you? Are you willing to step out of your comfort zone and embrace the moment before you? Or are you waiting to feel better before going for a walk, calling a friend, or getting up and getting dressed?

Life is just too darn precious to let the hours, days, weeks, and months pass you by. It's time to take back your life. Yes, living with a mental or physical disorder is challenging. But it's up to you to seize the moment, hold yourself accountable, and just do it. You'll be pleasantly surprised how empowered and proud you'll feel when you take action and accomplish what you set out to do.

Reflection Question: *What will you do today to seize the moment?*

_____

_____

_____

_____

Simple Sentences – Big Messages

"Be Glad. Be Good. Be Brave."

– Eleanor Hodgman Porter

Such simple sentences, yet each packed with a "punch." When I ponder, "Be Glad," I realize that, with just a tweak of perspective, I can be glad I was diagnosed with clinical depression and anxiety. Gladness arrives from knowing that my life purpose came through my illnesses.

Moving on to the next phrase, "Be Good," I unearth the need to be committed to my wellness so that I can live my purpose. "Be Good" might mean going to bed earlier, getting to the gym five times a week, or even choosing broccoli over French fries as part of my dining selection. I can think of numerous daily choices where this phrase, "Be Good," becomes part of my decision process.

And finally, "Be Brave." Brave is a strong word that means the most when it comes to dealing with a mental illness. We must be brave to try all the medication cocktails prescribed to us not knowing – but praying – that *this* cocktail will do the trick. Brave to pick up the pieces of a shattered life after an episode with the "beast." Brave to face the people who saw us at our worst. Brave to return to work. Brave to face the day when our illnesses urge us to stay in bed and isolate. And, most of all, brave when our thoughts are telling us to end it all. Yes, these two simple words, "Be Brave," say it best when you're faced with a mental health disorder.

Reflection Question: *What would it take for you to be glad, good, and brave?*

_____

_____

_____

_____

Mountain Tops & Valleys Are Both Part of Life

"Everything in life is what you make it."

– Alan Cohen

When I read this quote from one of my favorite authors, I thought back to a time when I didn't think this way. Somewhere, though, through the mountains and valleys of life, I've come to believe these words wholeheartedly.

There have been many times during the valleys of life when I became consumed, overwhelmed, and downright mad with the injustices of life. Years later when I looked back at those times, I recognized those valleys not only enhanced my character but empowered me as well.

Have you ever heard that if you break the cocoon away from a butterfly it hampers the butterfly's ability to build the strength in its wings to fly? It is in struggle that the butterfly prepares for flight. Well, we as humans also need the valleys in life to strengthen ourselves for the next life experience. Whenever we take time to reflect on our own life, it provides an opportunity to see how strong we've become.

When you struggle with a mental health disorder, whether for the first time or in a relapse, you are adding another level of strength from your struggle. This new strength can be utilized when you find yourself climbing toward a period at the top of the mountain of life; thus making the climb even more special.

Referring back to the original quote, remember it's important to perceive the experience as one that allows you to learn and grow into the individual you are today. The next time you find yourself in one of life's valleys, be sure to take time to acknowledge and feel the strength you are gaining from your experience.

Reflection Question: *Where do you find yourself today – in a* **valley** *or on* **top of a mountain?**

Rediscover Joy in Your Own Backyard

"When you recover or discover something that nourishes your soul and brings joy, care enough about yourself to make room for it in your life."

– Jean Shinoda Bolen

When I was first diagnosed with depression and anxiety, I recall vividly how my life was turned upside down. It seemed the only thing I could think about was my illness. At first, I lost a part of who I had been because I was so wrapped up in learning how to survive with a long-term, recurring illness. Activities and people I had enjoyed spending time with no longer mattered. What mattered most was getting well and staying in longer periods of recovery.

What I didn't recognize, though, was the importance of getting back to doing what I enjoyed before my diagnosis. Engaging in those activities and seeing people I looked forward to spending time with were a big part of my wellness journey. I needed to rediscover those interests that nourished my wellbeing and brought me joy. A return to crafts and baking provided endless hours of reprieve from worrying about whether my illness would return. An afternoon with a friend was a peaceful time for me to absorb her energy and love.

Making room in my life for activities and friends accelerated my recovery more than I could have ever imagined, and it could do the same for you.

Reflection Question: *What could you rediscover in your life that would bring back joy?*

_____

_____

_____

_____

Small Steps, Big Outcome

"Everything worthwhile was done by small steps taken one by one."

– J.D. Freeman

Dealing with depression and anxiety takes a tremendous amount of energy. These illnesses rob you of your desire, drive, and discipline. These three attributes are needed to become successful in whatever path you travel. For me, everything in my world becomes an overwhelming, heavy task when I find myself in the grips of depression. It takes up to five times longer for me to accomplish anything. Responsibilities and tasks that never fazed me in wellness now feel like climbing Mt. Everest.

What I've learned over the last 20 years of dealing with depression and anxiety is reflected in the quote above. I didn't have to conquer the climb in one month, one week, or one hour; I could conquer the climb one minute at a time.

And a few minutes at a time is how I tricked myself into getting back to "the climb" when it came to exercising. I would tell myself I only had to take a walk for five minutes today. Then I would literally set an egg timer, carry it with me, and walk just the five minutes. When the timer went off, I was done! The next day I would walk for ten minutes and extend my time a bit each day.

The payoff was a feeling of accomplishment and recognition that I was taking small steps toward wellness. This technique worked in other parts of my life as well. I would break any overwhelming task into small steps, achieve the step, add another step, and another. Before I knew it, I was on my way to completing the task. The next time you are faced with a task you don't want to do, give this technique a try.

Reflection Question: *What steps taken one- by- one could bring you closer to recovery?*

Life – A Great Balancing Act

"Healthy, successful living is not a mystery. It is simply a balancing act."

– Alan Cohen

According to Alan Cohen, author of *A Daily Dose of Sanity*, we each have three bodies with which we make our journey through life. We have physical, emotional, and mental bodies; and each requires care and attention. The physical body must be fed, rested, and exercised. The emotional body must be nourished with inspiration through love, music, and art. The mental body must be stimulated with ideas and projects.

Wow! What a revelation – especially for those of us dealing with the challenges of mental health disorders. You may notice as much as I do how all three of my "bodies" are impacted when I am in the midst of an episode. Physically I can't sleep, my appetite disappears, and I don't have the energy to exercise. Emotionally, I can't feel love, colors are dimmed, and nothing sounds the same. Mentally, I can't concentrate enough to read a sentence or even think clearly. My life is completely unbalanced, and basically, I want to throw the "*towel of life*" out the window.

I don't know about you, but I plan to take Mr. Cohen's words to heart and integrate them into my wellness plan. In conjunction with my medical treatment, I will remember to address the needs of my three bodies.

Mental illness is often referred to as an imbalance in our brain chemistry. Why not heed to healthy, successful living by providing your three bodies – physical, emotional, and mental – the nourishment, inspiration, and stimulation they need? Who knows, Mr. Cohen may be on to something!

Reflection Question: *What will it take for you to bring more "balance" to your own life?*

_____

_____

_____

_____

You Control What You Focus On

"In three words I can sum up everything I've learned about life, it goes on."

– Robert Frost

For many years I've been asked by consumers how to move forward with their lives after being diagnosed with a long-term mental health disorder. This question was one I often asked myself and others during my own recovery journey.

First, I allowed myself to be mad at the world. "This isn't fair! – Why me?" Once I gave myself ample time to feel disappointed, angry, and sad, I moved on to, "Okay, now what?" I embraced the place of acceptance in order to deal with the cards life had dealt me. Is life really fair anyway? Look around you, everyone copes with some kind of adversity.

Fortunately, I came across a statement that started to change my focus:

You will receive more of what you concentrate on.

This simple statement moved me from mourning the life I had once lived to appreciating the life I now had to live. While researching the power of appreciation, I found that gratitude is much more than a simple rote act. It is a consciousness to be maintained above all else. Its power derives from the most elementary law of metaphysics:

You will receive more of what you concentrate on.

Seeing these words twice in a short time provided the wake-up call I needed to get on with my life. Little by little my inner and outer worlds changed. My focus was no longer on what I had lost, but on what I had gained. I had a renewed appreciation for my small strides and accomplishments. My confidence returned, which further allowed me to achieve even bigger goals.

You, too, have the power to change your perspective if you really want to. Each time you feel yourself slipping back into the "poor me" pool – Stop, recognize the slip, and acknowledge three things you are grateful for in the present moment. Holding yourself accountable can make the difference.

Reflection Question: *What do you find yourself concentrating on?*

_____

_____

_____

Contagious Enthusiasm – It's Worth Catching

"None are so old as those who have outlived enthusiasm."

– Henry David Thoreau

How you embrace life makes all the difference in the world to yourself and to those around you. Take for example, *enthusiasm* which is defined as "a feeling inspiring zeal or fervor. " Many times enthusiastic people have crossed my path and what I've noticed is that their enthusiasm for life is contagious. All I need to do is open my heart and let it in!

Then there are the people who let life pass them by as they walk around with the weight of the world dragging them down every day. They seem to find fault in everything and everyone around them and nothing makes them happy. It's almost as though they've embraced misery and lack the desire to break the cycle of dread and disillusionment.

Unfortunately, for many of us a relapse can easily rob our own enjoyment and enthusiasm. When that happens, we need to keep reminding ourselves that it's the illness driving us down, and that "this too shall pass." Once recovery begins to "blow away the cloud of darkness," it is up to us to regain our passion for life and to find fulfillment in the things that make us smile and feel alive. With effort, we can return to a life of zeal and fervor.

I don't know about you, but I prefer to grow older with a bit of spring in my walk, a smile on my face, and a glow of enthusiasm that's contagious. Remember to put forth the effort to embrace an enthusiastic spirit and then share it. You never know who might be around to catch your renewed spirit!

Reflection Question: *What would it take to raise your enthusiasm level?*

Turn a Setback into a Comeback

"A setback is the opportunity to begin more intelligently."

– Henry Ford

Facing a relapse with a mental health disorder can be frustrating and down-right disappointing. These setbacks turn our lives inside out as we need to once again reclaim the life we lost. It comes down to how you go about reclaiming your life that will make the difference.

With the switch of attitude, you can turn a setback into a comeback – a comeback where you finally commit to following through on what it takes to remain in mental wellness. We are in an age where we are bombarded with information on how to stay physically and mentally fit. All you need to do is *do it.*

So what's the "do it"? Accept where you are today, and focus on keeping yourself well. Follow the treatment plans set out for you, keep learning about your disorder, explore what

36

others have done to stay well, and make a pledge to yourself to do whatever is necessary. Action is the antidote to inaction.

You have it within your power to start each day in action. Get up and greet the day – it's yours for the taking. Set out on your day with an attitude of gratitude, a smile on your face, and spring in your step. You can be assured you'll have a better day than you would have if you start out on the opposite side of life.

Remember – and believe – you are an intelligent, gifted individual. Begin sharing the gifts and abilities you have. You just might make this new day a brighter, happier one not only for yourself but for others as well. Go for it!

Reflection Question: *How do you plan to comeback from a setback?*

_____

_____

_____

_____

Recovery Takes More Than Pills

"Pills don't teach skills."

– Mary Moller

I had the good fortune of attending the American Psychiatric Nursing Association Annual Convention. During the convention I selected the Recovery Track to hear what's been happening towards that model. Amazing, inspiring, exciting, and hopeful are just a few words to express what's taking place in the nursing field concerning recovery.

Presentation after presentation focused on evidence-based practices of the recovery model and the difference they're making for consumers – who are fortunate enough to embrace them. Strategies ranged from moving the nursing station into an open environment and, allowing consumers to make meal selections, all the way to using mindfulness training with consumers. The energy around these changes was contagious. Nurse after nurse recounted evidence that this new model works. Hallelujah!

I've personally been talking about the recovery model for the last six years, and it is finally proven with real-time studies.

Recovery today is probable for 80 percent of those in treatment. But as the quote above states, it takes more than pills. Teaching consumers the skills and lifestyle changes needed to sustain recovery are key to their wellness. I don't know about you, but sustained recovery is my top priority.

Remember, it's not just the medication that you need to reach and maintain recovery – it is about learning new lifestyle skills!

Reflection Question: *What lifestyle skills do you need to fine tune?*

_____

_____

_____

_____

Find the Treasure in a Normal Day

"Normal day, let me be aware of the treasure you are. Let me learn from you, love you, and bless you before you depart. Let me not pass you by in quest of some rare and perfect tomorrow."

– Mary Jean Iron

Somehow in the haste and pace of life today, many people find themselves letting a "normal day" zip by without much notice or fanfare. There are "to do" lists with errands, responsibilities, and promises in need of attention, not to mention the challenges of the work/life balance. I don't believe life is supposed to be a constant struggle where you pack so much in during a day that you lose sight of embracing the day for the treasure it is.

Have you ever found yourself hanging on to life anxiously waiting for holidays or vacation days to take a break from the overwhelming feeling of your everyday schedule? You can't wait until calendar days pass so you can take a breather or escape. Without realizing it, you are wishing away days of your life that can never be recaptured.

So how do we begin to treasure the "normal days" of life? At the start of each day, make a conscious effort to appreciate the day. Before jumping out of bed, spend a few moments in giving thanks for this day, check on your attitude (your attitude is a choice), and learn to observe the many "joyful" moments that appear in any given day.

These extraordinary moments could be feeling the love of a baby's smile, a helping hand given to you, trying something new to eat for lunch, stopping to feel the sunshine on your face, or giving a compliment to a coworker. There are endless moments in a "normal day" to treasure. All you need to do is notice and appreciate them.

Reflection Question: *What have you noticed in your last "normal day"?*

To Accept or Not Accept

"Accept what comes to you totally and completely so that you can appreciate it, learn from it, and then let it go."

– Deepak Chopra

Acceptance of an illness that is misunderstood and carries stigma was incredibly difficult for me and for countless people I've spoken with. Yet, the longer we remained in a place of denial, a place of secrecy, and a place of self-pity, the longer it took us to heal from the inside out. Full acceptance for me did not appear until after my fourth bout with the "beast" (my endearing name for depression and anxiety) that barges into my life like a savage devouring my ability to engage in life.

Once I totally accepted that depression and anxiety were part of me and that they didn't define me, I was able to tame the "beast" and find ways to live. Today, I appreciate the "beast" because it taught me lessons that enhance my existence. The ability to appreciate each "well day" as a blessing has helped me create a life in the now rather than a life in the past or future.

Next came the lesson of letting go of worry. Between my first three episodes I was consumed with worry that the "beast" would return – and return with a vengeance it did. Finally, after my fourth bout, I decided to stop wasting "well time" by carrying the burden of worry. Instead, I let go of worry and decided to celebrate my time in wellness and to seek help in my time of illness. What a relief!

It's been 12 years since my last tangle with the "beast." I am convinced that the moment I fully accepted my illness, opened the air-tight closet to my secret, and relieved myself of worry, the "beast" became tamed and quieted. You too can find acceptance.

Reflection Question: *What lessons have you learned by accepting your disorder?*

Discover Your Life Lessons

"A wise man travels to discover himself."
– James Russell Lowell

Like most people, my life journey of self-discovery has included extreme highs and devastating lows. At the height of my journey were the lessons learned in parenting three amazing children, exceeding my expectations in my career, and sharing my faith with others who had lost their own faith. Those lessons are some of the sweetest parts of life – each lesson bringing with it the by-products of love, joy, and grace.

However, the lessons learned from the devastating lows have had a much greater impact on the person I've become. When I look in the mirror today, I see a woman of great character and strength. Individuals who have traveled a journey to recovery from any life circumstance see a similar face looking back at them. Whether your lows were created by illness, financial troubles, relationship ills, or job lost – you've found a way to recover and move on. Character and strength are part of your reward because you learned to pick up the pieces of a shattered life and move ahead to embrace an enriched life.

As you move forward in life, I encourage you to take time to really look at yourself in the mirror. Acknowledge and appreciate the individual you are today by reflecting on the extreme highs and devastating lows you've experienced. Taking time to do so is a sure way to improve your self-confidence as you face what life still has in store for you. Further, you have the reassurance that you've survived a circumstance and made it to the other side – recovery.

Reflection Question: *What characteristics have you discovered by looking at yourself in the mirror?*

_____

_____

_____

_____

From Survive to Thrive

"Great emergencies and crises show us how much greater our vital resources are than we had supposed."

– William James

Two events that individuals with mental health disorders learn to deal with are emergencies and crises – these calamities are part of the territory. Unfortunately, suicidal ideation is a cruel symptom that shows its ugly head during most relapses. I know because ideation consumed me during all four of my episodes, and I've heard from countless others about their similar experiences.

However, I also know from my experience and the personal stories of others, that in spite of those "dark times" not only did we survive – but we've learned to thrive.

Emergencies and crises became our training ground. The lessons learned during those times provided stronger foundations for life than we could have ever imagined. We became proactive in heading off future "dark times." We recognized triggers, made life-style changes, sought support earlier, and helped others in similar circumstances to do the same. We used our voices to become advocates as we shared our stories of hope and recovery with anyone who would listen. And finally we found others who are listening. We witnessed glimmers of light as we knocked down the walls of ignorance built around mental illness. With each conversation people became enlightened and less frightened of these often misunderstood illnesses.

There is still much work to be done, but never fear – *the thrivers are here!*

Reflection Question: *How have you thrived in spite of your disorder?*

_____

_____

_____

_____

Focus Hits the Bull's Eye – Recovery

"When the bull's eye becomes as big in your mind as an elephant, you are sure to hit it."

– Alejandro Jodorowsky

Through the years I've been fascinated by the Laws of Intention and Attraction. The more I read and studied these universal laws, the more I was able to manifest my desires. I've also come to learn that these universal laws are grounded in belief, expectation, motivation, and focus.

Yet when the "beasts" of depression and anxiety bring me to my knees and hold me hostage, the power of these universal laws evaporates into thin air as I barely hang onto life itself. What results from my tumultuous, emotional state of mind is the attraction and manifestation of isolation and hopelessness – the direct opposite state of mind I long for in recovery.

However, as medication and treatments begin to provide the "light of hope," my mind is once again focused on the bull's eye – recovery. I believe recovery is possible, I expect to recover, and I am motivated to do what I need to do. My intention once again attracts wellness.

At times, mental health disorders can be a vicious cycle of recurring episodes, but I've learned through my four bouts to keep focusing on my intention – sustained recovery. I've also come to recognize that sustained recovery takes an enormous effort on my part, which includes a combination of sleep, exercise, and nutrition as well as medication and therapy. You, too, can manifest recovery with the right intention. Give it a try!

Reflection Question: *What will it take for you to tap into the universal Laws of Intention and Attraction?*

Big Payoffs from Small Shifts

"Being of service to others is the rent we pay to be here."

– Anonymous

At times our illnesses are all consuming, isolating us from everything and everyone. I've found that one of the easiest ways to "get out of your head" at those times is to help someone else. I've witnessed how this strategy provided a springboard to recovery for others – and even for myself.

When we take the focus off of ourselves and serve others, a small shift happens that helps move us from mental illness to mental wellness.

For the last few years, I've prayed for daily guidance on how to serve people who cross my path. Sometimes I hear a whisper to deliver a kind word to a stranger walking by. Other times I feel a need to listen with compassion to the stranger, who shares her woes with me as we wait to be called for our appointments.

And I've seen how each small shift makes a difference. I've also observed how something as simple as holding the door or smiling and making eye contact with someone can lighten their day.

Challenge yourself to make a small shift. Look for simple ways to serve others every day. At the end of each day replay what you did and how it made you feel. It's a nice way to end your day rather than ruminating on your own mental health issues.

When you make the shift and find a way to help others, you'll feel better and be a little closer to mental wellness.

Reflection Question: *How have you served others lately?*

_____

_____

_____

_____

Take Back Your Day

"What I do today is important because I am exchanging a day of my life for it."

– Anonymous

My own experience with depression and anxiety stopped my world in its tracks and created a new realm of isolation and loneliness. At first, I was consumed with self-pity and self-doubt while my world became smaller and smaller; and I hid from family, friends, and colleagues. I noticed that I wanted my days to end, but nights were even worse. My illness became my life; it was all consuming. I was allowing depression and anxiety to steal away hours that turned into days which spilled into stolen months. Looking back, I now realize I exchanged a full decade of my life by allowing my illness to take over.

No more!

Today I approach each day as an opportunity to remain in recovery, even if it's just for that day. My personal strategies for a "well day" start the moment my eyes open from a good night's rest and include these specific steps, in order:

- Praying for wisdom to guide me during this new day
- Reading and reflecting on three daily devotionals
- Journaling a half page
- Exercising at the gym for an hour
- Taking my medications and vitamins
- Drinking a protein shake for breakfast

Sticking to this routine kick starts my day into full gear and allows me to take whatever comes up in stride. Just last week I woke with immense anxiety. I felt its tension the moment my head lifted from my pillow. Even though I wanted to jump out of my skin and hide from the world, I stuck to my routine and by the time I sat down with my protein shake, much of my anxiety had eased up. I no longer allow my anxiety to steal my day. What about you?

Reflection Question: *What strategies do you use to take back your day?*

_____

_____

_____

_____

Watch Your "Personal Drought"

"In dealing with those who are undergoing great suffering, if you feel burnout setting in, if you feel demoralized and exhausted, it is best, for the sake of everyone, to withdraw and restore yourself."

– Dalai Lama

After a hectic month of work and over-committing myself to both volunteer and social activities, I found myself on a slippery slope of feeling drained of my energy and spirit. During a discussion with a good friend, I realized that after giving so much of myself to everything and everyone, I needed to find a way to rejuvenate my mind, body, and spirit.

With the Internet at our fingertips we began searching for a place of peace and serenity. And as God would have it, not only did we find a spiritual retreat center at the Silver Bay YMCA in Silver Bay, New York, but there was a humor conference taking place at the center that exact weekend. Laughter, Lake George, and a labyrinth all found in the same place – perfect!

Just making the arrangements and cancelling all of my commitments for the weekend was a relief. I would have three days and two nights to take care of just me. Wow!

The weekend was filled with glorious laughter, time in the chapel meditating, walking the labyrinth, praying for guidance, and meeting new friends. With each passing moment, my spirits and soul were coming alive again.

When I arrived at the retreat, I felt like a flower wilting from a drought of self-care. Leaving the retreat, I felt centered, re-energized, and at peace. What a difference a weekend of self-care can make.

As I drove away from the center, I turned to read the entrance sign that I overlooked driving in. It read, "We hope you have an inspiring experience." I smiled and answered out loud, "I sure did!"

Reflection Question: *What one thing can you do this week to provide yourself with self-care?*

_____

_____

_____

Listen Carefully for the Whisper of Hope

"When the world says, "Give up."
Hope whispers, "Try it one more time."

– Author Unknown

I received an email from a colleague in Australia, who was traveling to a number of countries to talk about mental health recovery and ECT (electroconvulsive therapy better known as shock therapy). He asked me if there were any messages I wanted him to share with the various audiences he would be speaking to. After thinking about it for a minute, I replied with the following:

> **"The message I would like you to continue to drive home is: *Never lose hope. Recovery is possible even if someone has struggled for decades.*"**

During my own travels to speak about recovery, I've heard testimony after testimony from people who have found their way to recovery after years of struggling with mental health disorders. They felt hope and tried it one more time.

Both consumers and healthcare professionals need to remember that the human spirit is more resilient than we know. Once I heard a testimony from an individual who had been hospitalized for years. Eventually the hospital closed, and he was forced to go out into the world and live in a group setting. This individual got a job, began to make friends outside his mental health world, took up a hobby, rented an apartment, lived independently, found fulfillment, and became more than his mental health disorder. He was smiling with pride and joy as he shared his life journey with me.

Testimonials like his spells hope for all of us. Healthcare professionals need to plant hope in the individuals that they see. Once hope is planted and nurtured, there's a good chance it will blossom.

Reflection Question: *When was the last time you listened to the whispers of hope?*

_____

_____

_____

_____

Imaginations Can Dream BIG

"We all have the imagination to change our lives"

– Delia Ephron

Recently, **I attended a seminar** where the facilitator led an exercise that was both empowering and fascinating. He had us add five years to our current age then asked us to dream about what we had accomplished in those five years. We had a chance to share those dreams speaking about them in the past tense as though they had already happened. Wow!

Individuals in the seminar spoke about going back to school, starting a business, or a new career while others talked about getting married, traveling the world, or purchasing a new home. The goal of the exercise was to use our imaginations to create change in our lives.

When we were given permission to dream, our imaginations soared to new heights without limitations, fear, or uncertainty. The outcome of the exercise was smiling faces, renewed energy, and sheer excitement.

The next part of the exercise was to think about the first step to get to our dream. We were reminded that once you take the first step toward any change, the second step appears.

So now it's your turn to use your own imagination to dream BIG. Go outside in the sunshine, sit quietly, add five years to your current age, and dream about what your life was like in those five years. Now share it with someone you trust. You might try this exercise with a friend so you can both share your dreams with each other. Be sure you share your dreams in the past tense, like it has already taken place.

The only thing left is to take the first step towards creating the change in your life you saw in your dream. So dream BIG!

Reflection Question: *Who can you share your dream with?*

_____

_____

_____

_____

Recognizing the Can'ts and Cans that Make Life Easier

"Sometimes it is more important to discover what one cannot do, than what one can do."

– Lin Yutang

Traveling life's journey with a mood disorder is more interesting than other life journeys. Just like any journey, life with a mood disorder can require a bit of planning. In this case, it requires that you learn what works – and what doesn't – when it comes to sustaining recovery.

I don't know about you; but on my personal journey, I had to figure out what I just couldn't do any longer – and that was a harder pill to swallow than the dozen or so pills I was prescribed.

Here are seven "can'ts" and "cans" I've recognized. See if they bring a new perspective to your own journey:

1. You **can't** ignore personal accountability for keeping yourself in recovery; you **can** take more responsibility for yourself than your healthcare professionals do.

2. You **can't** expect to develop coping strategies in the middle of a stressful situation. You **can** develop those strategies before stress hits.

3. You **can't** ignore the tell-tale signs that you're heading for a relapse. You **can** ask for help when you need it – or even before you need it.

4. You **can't** ignore your need for rest and sleep since once sleep deprivation starts it's a slippery slope towards a relapse. You **can** maintain healthy sleep patterns.

5. You **can't** expect medication and talk therapy to keep you in recovery. You **can** discover the life-style changes you need to sustain your recovery.

6. You **can't** judge how well you are doing compared to someone else. You **can** compare how you feel today and how you were doing yesterday, last week, or last month.

7. You **can't** expect to go back to the way things were. You **can** embrace your "new normal" and forge ahead.

Reflection Question: *What **can't** and **can** you do today to strengthen your recovery?*

A Gift of Words to Last a Lifetime

"You have angels' wings surrounding you when you speak."

– Wendy Witherspoon

Following a keynote speech I delivered at a mental health retreat, I received confirmation of a loving force greater than anything I could have imagined. I shared gifts of experience, but the greatest gift was given to me. Following my presentation, a woman, who was sitting front and center during my speech, approached me and said, "You have angels' wings surrounding you when you speak." What she told me brought tears to my eyes and joy to my heart.

For the last seven years I have been delivering similar presentations, and, at times, sharing my darkest moments of depression have unnerved me. After the presentation, it took me hours to relax and feel peace again. I often wondered if those uncomfortable feelings would ever cease. Yesterday, I received my answer. When I speak of those darkest moments, I am wrapped in angels' wings. I am not standing alone when I share my experiences of a dark place that consumed me and brought me to my knees in desperation.

My faith has always been at the center of my life. During my darkest moments of depression and anxiety, the only place I felt relief was in a religious setting. During my four hospitalizations, whenever there was an opportunity to attend a religious service – no matter what the denomination – I was drawn to attend. It was during those services that, for a short time, my world was not consumed by suicidal ideation. I wondered if during those services the reason the suicidal ideation ceased for a short time was that, I was wrapped in angels' wings then, too. What a comforting thought!

Reflection Question: *How do you feel knowing that you may have angels' wings wrapped around you during your darkest moments of depression or anxiety?*

All It Takes Is a Question

*"You can't get 'yes' unless you **ask**!"*

– Carol A. Kivler

Coaching a number of executives this week reminded me of a simple yet essential communication strategy: ask for what you need or want. It's so simple, but then why is it so hard to *ask*?

Comfort in asking questions comes with maturity of thought. The moment we are born we are totally dependent on others to help to fulfill our needs. As we grew, we found ourselves becoming independent and believing that we needed to survive on our own without the help of others. However, as we matured, we recognized our state of interdependence, the state where we recognize the power of getting help from others. This is where asking for what we need and want comes into play.

When challenged with any health issue it is essential that you become comfortable with the communication strategy of asking. There will be times when you ask and you might not get a "yes." And there will be times when you may not have asked the right person, who could provide the "yes." But you *must* learn to ask to get a "yes."

For example, one executive spoke about wanting an international assignment with the company where he had worked for 11 years. He'd acquired a wealth of experience and received various promotions throughout his employment. I asked him if he had ever shared this desire with his manager and his answer was "no." Then I asked what was keeping him from sharing this goal with his boss. His answer was that he was afraid of his boss's response. My job was to prompt him to ask the question. And you already know the answer: "Yes! I think this would be a great next step in your career." His "yes" came from asking.

Reflection Question: *What question do you need to ask?*

Brush the Cobwebs off Your Dreams

"Cherish your visions and your dreams, as they are the children of your soul – the blueprint of your ultimate accomplishments."

– Napoleon Hill

Imagine waking up each morning with an excitement and passion that you haven't felt since you were diagnosed with a long-term mental health disorder. Somewhere along the line, your illness robbed you of your visions and dreams and you started settling for less.

Today I encourage you to take back your life and focus your intentions on realizing your forgotten visions and dreams. You need to start showing up each moment and commit to using all your gifts, talents, and brilliance in spite of your disorder. Why? Because once you do, you'll take back your life and start living the life you were meant to live.

When I was diagnosed with major depression and anxiety disorder, I let my dreams sit unattended for too many years. Then I met other consumers, in various walks of life, who not only dreamt the big dreams but who also had accomplishments that exceeded their dreams. By their example, I woke up and recognized how I was limiting my own life.

You too need to have a wake-up call to brush off the cobwebs on your own forgotten dreams. Revisit your dreams and share your intentions with others. You don't need to have every detail planned. You only need the first action step to you get started. Once you follow through on the first step, the second step will appear.

Is your dream to go back to school? Make the call to the school or pick up the course offerings. Do you want to play an instrument? Visit a music store or gather information about the instrument. Want to get a job? Create a resume or answer job ads.

It's up to you to take the first step!

Reflection Question: *What dream can you start working on?*

_____

_____

_____

_____

Your Experience Could Ease the Burden for Others

"We each have it within ourselves to make a difference – one call at a time."

– Carol A. Kivler

A s I sit at my computer to write this piece, I feel the deep concern felt by countless individuals around the world on any given day about this important question: Where do they find the information and comfort they need to "fight the battle of their life" against depression and anxiety?

I recently received a call that spoke volumes about my concern. The call was from a desperate husband, Dave, seeking information for his beloved wife, who had just been hospitalized for depression. The doctors were recommending ECT since she had been on a variety of medications without much relief. We set up a call for me to speak with his wife Lori in the hospital. Our conversation was open, honest, and meaningful. Lori and I connected on a level only possible because both of us had dealt with the same "beast."

I got another call from Dave. He was calling to let me know Lori was having her first ECT treatment as we spoke. More importantly, he was calling to ask questions about what to expect and how to support Lori moving forward. Hospitals are doing the best they can to prepare people to deal with the "beast," but more support is required for the people who, as Dave put it, "make it to the other side."

I encourage everyone who has been to battle and returned, to find ways to speak to others about your experience and instill hope in those people who are just beginning "the fight of their life" or just returning from it. These one-on-one conversations could provide the best treatment of all!

Reflection Question: *What would it take for you to reach out to others and provide the information and hope they seek?*

_____

_____

_____

_____

Change to Acceptance – Quite the Journey

"The first step toward change is acceptance...
Change is not something you do,
it's something you allow."

– Will Garcia

One thing we can be assured of is change. We change every single day because of our experiences. Whether it was a person we met, something we heard or read, a feeling that surfaced, or just another day lived – change is inevitable. All you need to do is look in the mirror – I mean really *look* at yourself. The person staring back at you seems like a stranger. I often find myself saying, "And who are you?" Time has a way of creeping up on our faces quicker than we would like to admit.

But when I step back and appreciate the changes that have happened over time, especially during my mental health journey, I marvel at how far I've come. The journey wasn't easy, pleasant, or fair. My four depression and anxiety episodes changed me in ways no other experiences could have. Not only have I accepted the changes those experiences provided, but I embrace the person I am today.

Until you live through your darkest and scariest moments, you cannot relate to others who have also traveled a similar journey. It is in those shared experiences that we develop empathy and compassion for others. And this world needs more empathy and compassion. That's a change we would all enjoy seeing in our world today.

Reflection Question: *What changes have you allowed to occur on your life journey?*

_____

_____

_____

_____

Peace and Contentment Is Up to You

"Until you make peace with who you are, you'll never be content with what you have."

– Doris Mortman

If you are like most people, there are times when your confidence wanes and you find yourself disappointed in who you are and how your life is going. Unfortunately, one of the symptoms of many mental health disorders is that your ability to like yourself *disappears*.

But then the sun begins to shine through, the symptoms go back into hiding, and you move into recovery. What I've noticed, though, is that when you begin comparing your life to others, you're never really content with what you have or who you've become. Remember, true peace and happiness comes from within, not from material things – and not from other people.

Also, you can get so wrapped up in worrying about the future or dwelling on the past that you let today go by without paying much attention to your everyday happiness.

Here are some strategies to help you find peace and contentment in the present moment. And here's the bonus – all these things are free for the taking. Do your best to embrace one or two each week.

1. Give a compliment to someone you come in contact with
2. Hug someone you love (including a pet)
3. Walk in nature and really listen to the sounds surrounding you
4. Stop to really look at a flower as it begins to blossom
5. Call a family member or friend you miss talking to
6. Drop by to see a neighbor you know doesn't get out much
7. Write a love note to yourself and read it a week later
8. Sit outside and watch the sunrise or the sunset

Reflection Question: *What will it take for you to step on your contentment journey?*

_____

_____

_____

_____

Connection with a Stranger

"The life I touch for good or ill will touch another life, and that in turn another, until who knows where the trembling stops or in what far place my touch will be felt."

– Frederick Buechner

Last year I was in London for business and then took time for a weekend holiday in Paris. As I embarked on touring a new city, I marveled at the history and the detail mankind put into buildings centuries ago. I was enchanted by the differences and the similarities in the people I met. I made it a point to engage in friendly conversation with others who had a twinkle in their eye or a smile on their face.

On the ride to the airport in a van full of passengers, I sat next to a middle-aged woman from Japan. For the first few miles we said nothing to each other. Yet my inner voice was urging me to strike up a conversation, so that is exactly what I did. During our conversation we discovered that we had

74

numerous connections, and before I knew it, I was handing her one of my pocket guides about recovery from depression. Toshi was touched by a gift from a stranger, and she said she knew who she was going to give the guide to in Japan.

This friendly, connecting behavior is a far cry from the woman I am when consumed by depression and anxiety. That woman wants to blend into the landscape, resist eye contact, and shut herself away from everything and everyone. I imagine there are many readers who can relate to the dramatic change in behaviors if you, too, are living with depression and anxiety.

Remember: reaching out to others can make a big difference!

Reflection Question: *When was the last time you reached out?*

_____

_____

_____

_____

It's Up to You to Reap the Benefits of Smiling

"Of all the things you wear, your expression is the most important."

– Janet Lane

Have you ever noticed how feelings of isolation, confusion, and hopelessness caused by depression and anxiety make smiling nearly impossible? Have you also observed that once you find yourself back on the road to recovery, your smile returns with a welcome relief? The relief comes because a smile is packed with loads of benefits!

Let's take a look at the anatomy of a smile:

- A smile makes you appear approachable, attractive, and approving. We are drawn to people who smile. We want to know a smiling person and figure out what is so good.

- A smile can brighten your mood or the mood of others. Smiling can trick the body into helping you change your frame of mind.

- Smiles are free and at your disposal at a moment's notice. The next time you are standing in line or waiting for someone or something – put on a smile and feel your stress melt away.

- A beautiful smile can help you feel self-assured. Smile and others listen to you because you appear confident.

- Smiles are contagious. A smiling person brings happiness with them and encourages others to smile as well.

- Smiles boost your immune system. When you smile, immune function improves possibly because you are more relaxed.

So remember to keep smiling – life is just too short for too many frowns!

Reflection Question: *When is the last time you caught a smile from someone?*

Today Is Your Cash in Hand – Spend It Wisely

"Yesterday is a canceled check; tomorrow is a promissory note; today is the only cash you have – so spend it wisely."

– Kay Lyons

Many individuals, who struggle with mental health disorders, spend so much time going over their past episodes worrying about future episodes that they have no energy left to live in the present.

If I've learned and absorbed anything from living with depression and anxiety, it's the importance of staying in the present moment. Whenever I find myself dwelling on my past or worrying about the future, I hold myself accountable and "self-correct." I remind myself that we can't change what has happened to us in the past, but we *do* have complete control over how we live today and tomorrow.

Fortunately, the best way to live today is to do everything within your power to stay in recovery. Individuals who

78

remain in recovery for the longest periods work on recovery *every single day*. They take responsibility for their mental wellness and made sustainable life-style changes.

When it comes to thinking about the future, these same individuals have put together a plan for how to handle an episode if and when it occurs; and they've shared that plan with their support network. This approach allows them to use the power of their own energy in the here and now instead of worrying.

Life, like the money in my wallet, seems to pass by at a rate faster than I would like. I remind myself that today is the only cash I have. So I've decided to do whatever I can to spend it wisely. I trust you will want to do the same!

Reflection Question: *What can you do differently to spend your "cash" wisely?*

All It Takes Is One Conversation at a Time

"Conversation by conversation – that's how the world changes."

– Daniel Pink

I was delighted to read this quote because I embrace its message with all my heart. Recently I was in a hospital hallway waiting for the nurse and student nurse to come out of my daughter-in-law's room. In the hallway were three other student nurses patiently waiting. Of course, I struck up a conversation and asked about their nursing studies.

If you knew me, you would know that just such a situation would lead me directly to a conversation about mental health disorders. These student nurses' next rotation was in the psych field. Bingo!

I immediately shared my mission in life, which is to educate others about the recovery model for the treatment of depression and anxiety. Their eyes widened as I talked about my history, and more importantly, told them how special they were for choosing nursing as their career.

Before I left them, I also told them about the other nursing schools where I've delivered my message. They were intrigued and promised to bring my name up to their professor. But I could do better than that! I gave them ten of my books, *Will I Ever Be the Same Again?* one for each of them and a few to pass on to their professors.

I may never know how my conversation impacted their careers, but I *do* know that I was in that hallway at that exact moment for a reason: to open up a conversation that may have impacted their perception of the recovery model for treating depression and anxiety.

Reflection Question: *When was the last time you had a conversation about recovery?*

_____

_____

_____

_____

A Year of Thankfulness – Dare to Begin

"All glory comes from daring to begin."

– Eugene F. Ware

Thanksgiving is a time to reflect on all the blessings of the past year. But why not make this coming year a year of thanksgiving every single day? As Ware's quote states, "All glory comes from daring to begin." Begin today with a conscious awareness of thankfulness for the people you meet, the experiences you have, and the little miracles that occur on a daily basis.

Take the time to say "thank you" to others; you just might make someone else's day a little brighter. Take time to thank God for peace of mind. Listen to the urgings of your heart. If you take time to listen, you will hear them clear as a bell. Embrace those urgings. When you do, you will find a purposeful life – and a purposeful life is a life worth living.

So I dare you to begin a new way of living life from this day forward – a life of true thankfulness. I can assure you, this coming year will be quite different from past years. When you find yourself celebrating Thanksgiving next year, you will reflect back on all the glory of a year lived with purpose.

Reflection Question: *What will it take for you to begin to live each day with thankfulness?*

Can We Count on You This Week?

"Doing Good Does You Good."
— Slogan for Mental Health Awareness Week

For the last 20 years, the first week in October has been designated as Mental Health Awareness Week – a week dedicated to opening the eyes, minds, and hearts of the general population concerning mental health disorders. Twenty- two years ago when I was first diagnosed with depression and anxiety, rarely was I able to mention my illness. These disorders were shrouded in shame, guilt, and secrecy.

However, it's now the 21st century and the world is beginning to recognize mental health disorders not just as diseases that need treatment; but diseases that, when managed properly, can lead to recovery and a productive life.

This is where each of us living in recovery can make a difference. As the quote states, we personally benefit from doing what we can during this week – or any week. We can provide our testimonies of recovery, take part in awareness events, and support others still struggling to see a brighter day. No one should have to struggle alone with hopelessness.

Organizations like National Alliance on Mental Illness (NAMI) and Depression and Bipolar Support Alliance (DBSA) are waging awareness campaigns across the country. Check out their websites at www.nami.org and www.dbsalliance.org to locate the events in your area.

When I look back over the last 22 years, I have witnessed forward motion in small steps. We still have a long way to travel; therefore, the steps need to increase in size so more and more individuals seek treatment and reach recovery. The good you do this week will surely do you good, so make the effort!

Reflection Question: *What good will you continue to do for mental health awareness?*

Even Strangers Need a Friend

"There can be no greater or simpler ambition than to be a friend."

– Mark Nepo

Iwas on a flight from Chicago to Philadelphia. I settled into my middle seat with two small books purchased at the airport. Those two details in themselves are strange – I never select a middle seat, and I rarely purchase two books at the airport.

I began reading. From my peripheral vision, I noticed the young woman sitting in the window seat kept opening and closing the shade and then cradled her head in her hands. She repeated the same routine every couple of minutes. I stopped reading for a minute, and she turned to me. She asked, "Do you fly frequently?" "Yes," I answered. She shared how petrified she was of flying; her anxiety was through the ceiling. She said she was afraid the engines would catch on fire and we would crash. Bingo! So that's why she kept opening and closing the shade. Anxiety sure has a way of wrapping us up in fear.

As a person who knows anxiety well, I immediately became a friend to a stranger. I spoke to her about fears and anxiety as I held her hand and assured her we would land safely. Then it occurred to me that the other book I had purchased was a pocket guide on feeling secure. Wasn't that interesting? I had no idea what made me even pick up that book! I gave it to her as a gift.

Then, two days ago when I spoke to an executive from Mexico, he shared a new term with me that is widely used in his country – "Godincidence." It's clear now why I had the middle seat and why I purchased the pocket guide.

Reflection Question: *What "Godincidence" have you noticed lately?*

_____

Influencing Others – It's About Examples

"Example is not the main thing in influencing others. It is the only thing."

– Albert Schweitzer

I had the opportunity to speak to a Neumann University's psychiatric nursing class about my experience with depression, anxiety, and the treatment option electro-convulsive therapy (ECT). My goal was to influence their upcoming healthcare careers by providing a positive example of recovery while also dispelling the misconceptions surrounding ECT.

As I looked out into a sea of future nurses, I realized what an awesome responsibility these young men and women have chosen as their life profession. The hunger in their eyes for information was evident. Their questions opened a line of discussion that brought a change in their perspective while adding a new level of understanding to the possibility of recovery and ECT as a treatment option.

While I spoke of the darkest moments of my depression and the fear I felt, their eyes widened with understanding. They had a glimpse of the influence psychiatric nurses had on my experience. I believed that by sharing my story, their level of empathy and compassion for their future patients blossomed.

Never underestimate how your example could influence others. You may not have the opportunity to speak to a room full of future nurses, but you could find yourself speaking to one nurse or healthcare professional. I encourage you to share your experiences. By your example, you have the capability to influence the care of countless others.

Reflection Question: *What mental health experience could you share that could influence others?*

Energy, Enthusiasm, and Colors – Zapped

"Sometimes our light goes out but is blown into flame by another human being. Each of us owes deepest thanks to those who have rekindled this light."

– Albert Schweitzer

Depression and anxiety not only extinguish my light of energy and enthusiasm, they also dim the colors in my world. However, I am fortunate because I've have had so many human beings, from family and friends to healthcare professionals, who have rekindled my light and brought me back to the living and at times to the thriving.

When we find ourselves in a lifeless, colorless existence, it can be daunting and exhausting. Consequently, this is when our support team can make all the difference. Yet it's during these times that we find it most difficult to ask for help, or even let others help us when they offer.

Interestingly enough, I recall feeling embarrassed when family and friends came to visit me in the hospital, and at the same time, felt enlightened because of their visit. They brought the outside world in to my hospital world. For a "blink of a moment" I saw a flicker of their light.

So what's a person to do?

I recommend opening up a discussion with your family and friends during your recovery to let them know you acknowledge and appreciate their support during your time of need. Tell them that even though you didn't seem receptive to their visits or calls while you were in an episode, their presence and love eased your social isolation.

Reflection Question: *When was the last time you thanked the people who helped rekindle your light?*

_____

_____

_____

_____

Gaining Comfort by Letting Go

"Courage is the power to let go of the familiar."
– Mary Byrant

During this holiday season, it is easy to fall back on traditions that no longer fit your life. The quote above reminds us that it takes courage to let go of things we are accustomed to doing or expecting.

Take for example, gift giving. Over the years my gift giving list grew longer and longer. The joy of gift giving became more of a chore than a joy. So, a few years ago, I decided most of my family and friends have everything they really need. Instead, I decided to make a donation to a worthy cause in honor of many of my family members and friends. I remember wondering how this unfamiliar gift idea would be received. To my delight and surprise my idea was embraced with opened arms and loud " thank you's."

Let's look at another example. This year my beloved sister, who usually sends out more than 180 Christmas cards, called to "test the waters" with me on how I felt about not sending out cards. I could hear her concern and apprehension about letting go of this tedious process. And I am happy to report she had the courage to let go of the familiar and decided not to send cards this year. Interesting enough, by the end of our conversation, I actually heard a sigh of relief.

Finally, think about the amount of stress we create for ourselves by trying to do it all and be everywhere during the holiday season. Learning to say "no" to past traditions and even some invitations takes courage, but the payoff is a holiday spent well!

Reflection Question: *What familiar pastime do you need to let go?*

_____

_____

_____

_____

Worry Less Strategies – We Could All Use

"Let us be of good cheer, remembering that misfortunes hardest to bear are those which never come."

– James Russell Lowell

With mood disorders comes anxiety, and with anxiety comes worry. Have you ever thought about how much time you spend worrying? How you worry about things that never materialize yet consume your waking moments, at times paralyzing your thoughts and bodies and wasting your time and energy?

I recall a colleague mentioning that she wished there was a pill she could take to stop her from worrying. All I could think of was I take enough pills already to manage my symptoms including pills to deal with the side effects of the first pill prescribed. There must be a better way to stop all this worrying.

So after a little creative thinking with others, we came up with three more positive strategies:

- Create a "worry box." Find a small box and decorate it to your liking. When worry creeps up, write it down on paper, and place the worry in your box for good keeping. Come back a few days later, and see if that worry came about.

- Limit the amount of time you spend worrying by creating a "worry hour." Allow yourself to only worry during that hour. If you catch yourself worrying at any other time, stop yourself, and hold onto that worry for your next worry hour. Soon you will find an hour is too long.

- Keep a journal of your worries. By writing them down first you get them out of your head. Then you have a way of tracking them to see what percentage of your worries come true. I assure you it will be a low percentage.

Remember: joy and cheerfulness in life are yours for the taking. Be sure to take hold of them.

Reflection Question: *What worry can you place in your "worry box" today?*

Abundant Lessons – Within Your Reach

"Today is yesterday's pupil."

– Thomas Fuller

Many years ago I heard someone say, "We must all become life-long learners because the road to success is always under construction." Once you reflect on this statement, you begin to realize that every day is an opportunity to become a student.

If you keep your eyes, ears, heart, and mind open at all times, you will be pleasantly surprised at the abundance of *lessons* within your reach. I have learned to take daily experiences and glean *the lesson* from them within hours. You, too, can achieve the same learning.

Take a look at these examples:

- You lend a friend money; your friend doesn't make any effort to pay you back.
  The lesson: *Either you never lend money again or, if you*

lend money, view it as a gift and don't expect it to be returned.

- You were driving your normal route to work when you came across a detour, which cut time off your commute. **The lesson:** *Don't settle for the first route, be willing to explore other ways of getting places.*

- You share something in confidence with someone and before you know it, that person tells someone else. **The lesson:** *Sharing "fragile" information with another person first requires that you develop a trusting relationship.*

- You are at work completing your tasks the way you always do, when a coworker comes by and shows you a shortcut to the task. **The lesson:** *Be open to new ways of doing things or recognize there is more than one way to complete a task.*

The experiences you encounter will continue to provide the lessons you need to keep learning. Just remember to be open and willing because you never know when the next lesson is within your reach!

Reflection Question: *What lesson have you learned lately?*

_____

_____

_____

Music to Our Ears

"Hopeful expectation has a way of warming our hearts and spirits."

– Carol A. Kivler

I had the honor of presenting at the American Psychiatric Nurses Association (APNA) convention in Pittsburgh. This particular group of healthcare professionals has always held a special place in my heart. During my hospitalizations nurses were the ones who made all the difference in my darkest moments of depression and anxiety.

The overriding themes of the APNA convention were themes that are near and dear to my heart: fighting stigma and promoting recovery. It was music to my ears. One of the "founding mothers" of APNA, Grayce Sills, shared examples of how psychiatric disorders are finding their way into mainstream America. She read a marriage announcement from the New York Times Social Section that included where the couple had met – at a treatment center where they were both recovering from bouts of anxiety and depression. Ms. Sills went on to mention a well-known coach who had left his post to receive treatment for depression. He returned to coaching for another team after disclosing his commitment to his own mental wellness. Ms. Sills, now in her 90s, believes we are on the "tipping point" of how others view mental illness. I agree!

We also heard about how the medical model for treating mental health disorders is being replaced with the recovery model. Over and over I listened as these "angels of healthcare" spoke about *"moving from mental illness to mental wellness."* Their messages were even more music to my ears and to anyone who has faced challenges to their mental wellness.

When I returned from the APNA convention, I was filled with **hopeful expectation** about the changes we are about to witness in the mental health field. Let's keep up our efforts so these changes take root!

Reflection Question: *How can you promote the recovery model?*

Self-Discovery: An Awesome Journey

"You can live a lifetime and, at the end of it, know more about other people than you know about yourself."

– Beryl Markham

This quote hits home for so many people including me. For a long time, I was so busy attending to other people's needs, spending countless hours listening to what they had to say, and taking time to fulfill their wants, that I didn't know myself. Finally, ten years ago, I found myself on the path to self-discovery by identifying my own likes, dislikes, wants, needs, and interests.

I recognized that I knew little about what made me happy or sad. I kept asking myself questions that I couldn't answer. And they were easy questions such as; "What's your favorite thing to do on a rainy day?" or "Where would you like to go on your next vacation?" Like many women, I was so preoccupied with everyone else's answer that I didn't pay attention to my own needs, wants, and desires.

100

Well, not anymore!

Today, I take time to listen to my inner spirit. It had been there all along; I just never shut off others' voices long enough to hear my own inner voice. Now I embrace my own answers and opinions, and I've gained confidence in sharing them with others. It's been an awesome journey!

What about you? Are you so caught up in others' needs and wants that you've forgotten about your own? If so, I urge you to start listening attentively to your own inner voice today. Self-discovery can lead you to a gratifying life.

Reflection Question: *What is your inner voice saying to you right now?*

More Than Words Can Provide

"Those who bring sunshine to the faces of others cannot keep it from themselves."

– James M. Barrie

I had the opportunity to stop by and meet a family that I had been speaking with over the phone for a number of weeks concerning their son's depression and anxiety. Josh had struggled for six years with no relief. This family was at the end of their rope. How many of us have found ourselves in the same place – frustrated, tired, and overwhelmed by an illness that took a "wrecking ball" and destroyed the life we once knew?

What words could I say that would make this family and Josh feel any better or see a glimmer of light? Interestingly enough, I learned it wasn't what I could say – it was what I could provide:

- **A listening ear.** This family needed to share their story and fears with someone without being judged or lectured to. As they recounted six years of torment, their faces softened and their voices began to relax. I had to say very little, I just had to listen with empathy and love.

- **Many hugs.** I entered their home as a stranger who wanted to ease their pain and fears and share as many words of encouragement and support as I could offer. Again, I noticed I didn't need to say much. My hugs said it all. As I embraced Josh, his mother, and his father, I passed on my energy of hope and love in my hugs. Isn't that why we are on earth to begin with?

Strangely enough, when I left Josh's home I didn't feel sad, instead I felt connected and at peace with the world.

Reflection Question: *Who in your circle of influence needs a listening ear and many hugs?*

Start Talking – Others Are Listening

"You must be the change you wish to see in the world."

– Mahatma Gandhi

Recently, I had the chance to talk with a group of people from all walks of life. As is so often the case, I was asked, "What do you do?" This question always gives me the opportunity to open peoples' eyes, minds, and hearts to the truth about mental illness.

Because I am a consumer advocate first and foremost, I shared my journey of living and recovering from depression and anxiety. This small group was surprised to hear the statistics and truths surrounding mental illnesses because this is something most people don't openly talk about. I hope these conversations helped overcome the stigmas about mental illness that they had and changed their attitudes as well.

What really amazed me during these conversations was that many of these individuals had family members with mental health disorders whether it was a wife, a son, or a mother. And, even though they were personally impacted by mental illness, they had misunderstandings and doubts about what their loved ones went through during their illnesses.

I did my best to explain that sustainable lifestyle changes – the same kind of changes you would make if you were diagnosed with a physical illness – can lead to longer periods of recovery. It was an "aha moment" that led to more conversation and more questions.

We can all start a dialogue with the people around us about mental illness and how it impacts us and our loved ones. And believe me, people are listening. By starting the conversation and sharing our experiences, we can help change the world!

Reflection Question: *What's one of your conversation starters?*

_____

_____

_____

_____

Accomplishments Increase Self-Confidence

"Nothing builds self-esteem and self-confidence like accomplishment."

– Thomas Carlyle

My beloved nine - year - old grandson, J.R., attended a camp for children with disabilities called, Lose the Training Wheels. The camp provides bicycle training for children with disabilities. J.R's disability is on the autism spectrum. We'd been trying to teach him how to ride a two-wheeler for more than two years.

This wonderful camp has an 80 percent success rate because of a brilliant engineer, who designed special bikes that teach children to balance effortlessly. Seeing children make small strides each day and move closer and closer to independent cycling is a dream come true for the parents sitting in the gym watching their children.

Every day my daughter sent me a video recording J.R.'s progress from her iPhone. By Wednesday, only three days into his experience, J.R. took his first solo ride around the gym. When I watched the video on my computer, tears streamed down my face as I sent prayers of thanksgiving to God.

J.R. called on his way home with such enthusiasm and pride, "Grammy, I did it! Riding a bike is so much fun. I can't wait to go back to camp tomorrow." Coming from J.R., those words were music to my ears. You see J.R. shows very little emotion towards anything. As Carlyle's quote states, accomplishment builds self-confidence. Because of his accomplishment, J.R.'s self-confidence is soaring. We can't wait to see what he will have the confidence to try next.

For those of us challenged by mood disorders we know far too well how self-confidence flees when we are in the midst of an episode. In those times, we need to remember, that we might accelerate the return of our self-confidence by acknowledging our daily accomplishments – no matter how big or small.

Reflection Question: *What have you accomplished today?*

Journaling is a Natural Release Strategy

"My journal is my constant companion. It is never far from my reach. It is a front porch of solace and retreat when I am tired and weary."

– Nicole Johnson

This morning I awoke feeling the need to sit down with my journal. Like many people, I find that journaling produces amazing results. When I journal, my pen can't seem to keep up with the flow of thoughts and feelings that flood the page. As I wrote, I realized that I hadn't been doing a good job of dealing with what life had been throwing at me for the last couple of weeks.

Before I began to journal, I remembered a passage from Anne Frank's, *A Dairy of a Young Girl*, where she wrote, "The nicest part is being able to write down all my thoughts and feelings; otherwise I might suffocate." This morning I felt so weary; I actually thought I would suffocate if I didn't release everything weighing me down.

After four pages of writing, I knew exactly what was going on with me. Technology issues lead to stress, which lead to health concerns; my work/life balance had been impacted by placing too many "to do's" on my checklist; and my children and grandchildren are still dealing with major health concerns. Finally, friendships had been rocked by misunderstandings. My enthusiasm and energy were tapped out, no wonder I was in need of a retreat and some quiet time for journaling.

If you ever find yourself disconnected, overburdened, or out of sorts, sit down in a quiet place, put your pen to paper, and release your feelings in your journal. Your burdens won't go away, but somehow, they won't feel as heavy once you acknowledge them and write them down. Give it a try!

Reflection Question: *What burdens could you release by journaling?*

_____

_____

_____

_____

Self-Forgiveness Is the Best Commitment of All

"I blew it and I knew it, now I forgive myself!"
– Carol A. Kivler

As we bring another year to a close, we hear talk of New Year's resolutions. Yet, most resolutions die off within 30 days or less. So I have a better idea. Instead of making a resolution, why not make a commitment this year – a commitment to yourself of self-forgiveness.

In a world that can be both negative and critical, grant yourself the gift of self-forgiveness. Each time you make a mistake, use poor judgment, or don't follow through, be quick to repeat the statement: "I blew it and I knew it, now I forgive myself!" It will be easier to move into action instead of beating yourself up. The world and others do enough of that – you surely don't need to do it as well.

Making this commitment will not only bring you greater self-acceptance, but it will improve your self-esteem and self-love. And I don't know about you, but we could each use a larger dose of those qualities. So give it a try.

I promise you a peaceful year where your own self-acceptance will radiate outward and attract more of what you want in life.

The benefits of self-forgiveness are just one commitment away – take the leap – and reap all life has to offer you in this new year.

Reflection Question: *How can you show more forgiveness to yourself this year?*

_____

....

_____

_____

One Word Can Make a Difference

"A good beginning makes a good end."

– English proverb

In one of my daily devotionals, I read about selecting **one word** that I could embrace throughout the holiday season. This **one word** would act as my guide and anchor through a season that, at times, can become hectic. This word would help me get off to a good start for the holidays and hopefully, see me ending the season on a good note as well.

So on the first of December, the word I chose was "**joy**." Throughout the day I brought that one word – **joy** – to my conscious mind. As I stood in line at the bank and waited to purchase Christmas gifts, I continued to bring **joy** front and center. What I experienced was amazing. My actions and tone of voice became **joyous**. I found myself spreading **joy** to everyone I came in contact with throughout the day. As I wished strangers a **joyous** Christmas, I noticed other people beginning to smile.

I shared the **one word** concept with my partner, so he gave it a try. The **one word** he chose was "**ease**." He changed his attitude and was excited that evening when he shared how his day turned out. With **ease** he was able to get more done in one day than he had in an entire week!

Here are some words to consider if you'd like to try the one word experiment this holiday season: *wonder, togetherness, spirit, reverence, play, love, joy, innocence, heart, generosity, fun, flow, ease, connection, celebration, appreciation, vitality, abundance.*

You will be happy to learn how *a good beginning can truly make a joyful end*!

Reflection Question: *What **word** will you choose to create a good beginning and end to this holiday season?*

_____

_____

_____

_____

Turn Resentment into Gratitude – It's Up to You

*"Gratitude helps you to grow and expand:
gratitude brings joy and laughter into your life
and into the lives of all those around you."*

– Eileen Caddy

From the start, most people diagnosed with a mental health disorder find it hard to be grateful. Instead of feeling gratitude, thoughts of resentment and disappointment surface first. How do I know? Not only have I had those negative feelings myself, but I've talked to others who have felt similarly. Until individuals work through these debilitating negative thought patterns, they will be held back from living a life of gratitude, and as the quote above states, "Gratitude brings joy and laughter into your life."

So how can you be grateful for a mental health diagnosis? By recognizing the lessons learned and the gifts delivered, you can transform resentment into gratitude.

One lesson I learned through my challenge with depression and anxiety is to *live in the moment*. When I live in the moment, I look at my diagnosis differently. I appreciate the little things – a green light when I am running late, a call from a friend at the exact right moment, and a sunny afternoon to enjoy lunch outside.

Gratitude is the perspective of viewing the little things as blessings. And you know what I've noticed? The more grateful I become, the more blessings I find coming my way. So give it a try – start counting your blessings and watch them multiply!

Refection Question: *What are three blessings you enjoyed just today?*

Self-Discipline – Aids Recovery

"Commitment – the more you have invested in something, the less likely you are to let it fail."

– Rory Vaden

During the last month I was intrigued by the book, *Take the Stairs – 7 Steps to Achieving True Success*, by Rory Vaden. I began reading the book with the international executives that I coach in mind. However, the more I read about the seven steps, the more I realized how aligned these steps are with the recovery model for sustained wellness in dealing with a mental health disorder.

The overriding theme for the seven steps is: self-discipline. Rory contends that, "Discipline creates freedom – freedom to do anything." Wow! What an empowering declaration. Since depression and anxiety steal your power, this statement caught my attention; and I trust it will capture yours.

These seven steps, if used consistently, can help you remain in recovery for longer periods of time.

1. *Sacrifice* – set aside short-term discomfort for long-term results.

2. *Commitment* – change from the question "Should I?" to "How will I?" is the mindset shift that makes all the difference.

3. *Focus* – keep your mind on recovery and minimize distractions.

4. *Integrity* – all of creation follows a simple and powerful pattern: "You think it, you speak it, you act it, it happens."

5. *Schedule* – learn that focused effort is amplified by appropriate timing and regimented routine.

6. *Faith* – choose to believe that all that is happening today – good or bad – is part of an ultimately greater plan.

7. *Action* – realize the right mind-set preceded proper movement, but the bottom line of seeing change and results in your life is your need to act.

Recovery seldom comes to individuals unwilling to hold up their end of the work that needs to be done. Get started today.

Reflection Question: *What steps have you already mastered?*

_____

_____

Choice and Action the Unbeatable Team

"We must be willing to get rid of the life we've planned, so as to have the life that is waiting for us."

—Joseph Campbell

If you are a planner like me, you have certain goals you want to achieve and things you want to do. Somehow, though, life doesn't always work out the way you planned. When this occurs you have choices to make:

- You can become miserable, mad at the world and throw the "towel in" on life.
- You can become resentful and make everyone uncomfortable to be around you.

OR

- You can adjust your goals to fit the circumstances you now find yourself in.
- You can develop an attitude of appreciation and embrace your life ahead.

118

Freedom of choice is your birthright. No one can choose for you – choosing your path is entirely up to you.

Diagnosed with a life-long illness can be devastating, disappointing, and debilitating. It takes time to absorb the impact and accept the illness. Have you ever been around individuals who haven't moved to acceptance? These individuals are wading through life half alive, limiting their potential, and feeling sorry for themselves. They blame everyone and everything for their circumstances.

Flipside to the individuals who have gone to Plan B in life. Their lives are filled with a new purpose, a new appreciation, and a new outlook. They are more alive than before their diagnosis. They have chosen to adjust their goals or create entirely new goals; they have chosen to live life differently in spite of what life has thrown at them.

So where are you with your life plan? Can you identify with any of the choices above? Do you have it within yourself to choose a different plan moving forward? I am a firm believer you do. Choice and action go together. Go for it!

Reflection Question: *What action can you take today to live the life that is waiting for you?*

_____

_____

_____

Resources

National Alliance on Mental Illness (NAMI)
www.nami.org – (800) 950-6264

Depression and Bipolar Support Alliance (DBSA)
www.dbsalliance.org – (800) 826-3632

Esperanza
Hope to Cope with Anxiety and Depression (magazine)
www.hopetocope.com – (877) 575-4673

www.HealthyPlace.com – Largest consumer mental health site

SAMHSA
Substance Abuse and Mental Health Services Association
www.samhsa.gov

www.CourageousRecovery.com – (609) 882-8988

Follow Carol on Social Media:
blog
www.carolkivler.com

Facebook
www.facebook.com/CarolKivler

Twitter
www.twitter.com/CarolKivler

Google +
plus.google.com/u/0/116170830203283686927/posts

Pinterest
http://pinterest.com/carolkivler/

Courageous Recovery Update - newspaper
http://paper.li/CarolKivler/1319246463

Linked In
www.linkedin.com/pub/carol-kivler/a/602/488

Feed Burner
feeds.feedburner.com/Carolkivler

Amazon Author Page
www.amazon.com/Carol-A.-Kivler/e/B005GWWAT6/

You Tube
www.youtube.com/user/CarolKivler

Carol A. Kivler, MS, CSP

Carol is president of Kivler **Communications**, a corporate training and international executive coaching firm. Since 1994, Carol has served over 100 companies nationwide and has coached over 600 executives worldwide. Through Courageous Recovery, a division of her firm, Carol focuses her presentations in the mental health field by sharing her message of hope and recovery.

Carol has been a member of the NAMI Mercer Board of Directors for ten years and an In Our Own Voice (IOOV) presenter. In 2008, she received the Garden State Seed of Hope Award from New Jersey Monthly Magazine for her tireless efforts educating and advocating in the mental health field. In 2013, Carol was nominated for a WEGO Health Activist Award for her blogging in the mental health field.

She is an active participant in the American Psychiatric Nurses Association Consumer Advisory Panel, a member of the Nursing Sub-Committee of the International Society for ECT and Neurostimulation (ISEN) and part of the ISEN Patient Advisory Committee.

Carol received her bachelor's degree in business education from The College of New Jersey and her master's degree in human resource education from Fordham University. Carol has also received the Certified Speaking Professional designation from the National Speakers Association.

Carol is a popular keynote and workshop speaker at mental health conferences, events, and facilities. She presents grand rounds at hospitals, medical/nursing schools, continuing education programs, staff professional development, and CEU/CME courses. She is also an in-demand speaker at consumer conferences across the country.

Carol is a riveting, authentic, and memorable speaker. Her high-energy and compelling presentations change thinking and inspire participants to reach beyond the myths and stigma surrounding mental illness.

Carol donates 50 % of her speaking fees and 15% of book sales to NAMI Mercer, New Jersey, a nonprofit organization of families and individuals dedicated to improving the quality of life of people affected by mental illness.

Presentation Topics

Mental Health Recovery Boosters – *New Program*
The ABCs of Recovery from Mental Illness
Women and Depression
Putting the Face of Hope on Depression
The Other Side of Psychosis
Demystifying ECT: What You Don't See in the Movies
Don't Tell Anyone I've Had ECT-It's My Secret

Other Books by Carol A. Kivler

Blessings: My Journal of Gratitude
This interactive book provides a heartfelt way to preserve your recollections and move more deeply into self-reflection with your own blessings, to guide you with inspiring words, captivating watercolors, and different textures.

Will I Ever Be the Same Again?
Transforming the Face of ECT (Shock Therapy)
Deeply personal and honest, Carol takes readers through her debilitating journey through clinical depression. She shares her medication-resistant experiences, electroconvulsive therapy and ultimate recovery.

The ABCs of Recovery from Mental Illness
A handy pocket guide of 26 non-medical strategies that consumers can incorporate into their treatment plan to sustain wellness. Carol provides valuable information for consumers, their loved ones and health care providers.

You can reach Carol at
(609) 882-8988 or
Carol@CourageousRecovery.com
Website: www.CourageousRecovery.com
Blog Site: www.CarolKivler.com

CPSIA information can be obtained at www.ICGtesting.com
Printed in the USA
BVOW012207190513

321114BV00005B/12/P